The Passive AGGRESSIVE Colouring Book

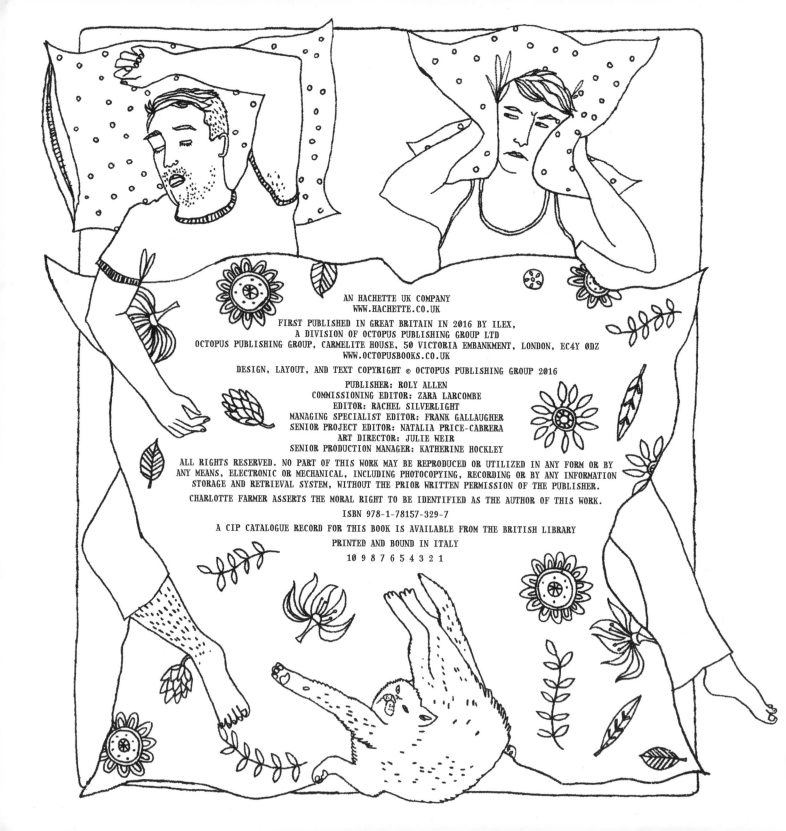

AN HACHETTE UK COMPANY
WWW.HACHETTE.CO.UK

FIRST PUBLISHED IN GREAT BRITAIN IN 2016 BY ILEX,
A DIVISION OF OCTOPUS PUBLISHING GROUP LTD
OCTOPUS PUBLISHING GROUP, CARMELITE HOUSE, 50 VICTORIA EMBANKMENT, LONDON, EC4Y 0DZ
WWW.OCTOPUSBOOKS.CO.UK

DESIGN, LAYOUT, AND TEXT COPYRIGHT © OCTOPUS PUBLISHING GROUP 2016

PUBLISHER: ROLY ALLEN
COMMISSIONING EDITOR: ZARA LARCOMBE
EDITOR: RACHEL SILVERLIGHT
MANAGING SPECIALIST EDITOR: FRANK GALLAUGHER
SENIOR PROJECT EDITOR: NATALIA PRICE-CABRERA
ART DIRECTOR: JULIE WEIR
SENIOR PRODUCTION MANAGER: KATHERINE HOCKLEY

ISBN 978-1-78157-329-7

A CIP CATALOGUE RECORD FOR THIS BOOK IS AVAILABLE FROM THE BRITISH LIBRARY

PRINTED AND BOUND IN ITALY

10 9 8 7 6 5 4 3 2 1

# The Passive AGGRESSIVE Colouring Book

## (FOR PEOPLE WHO JUST DON'T GET THE WHOLE CALM THING)

### CHARLOTTE FARMER

ilex

1. DAWN CHORUS   2. Bathroom Blues

3. Kale Fail   4. Love Your Job

5. GOOD NEIGHBORS

6. How Does your Garden Grow

7. MINDLESSNESS Snacks 8. Rubbish Yoga

9. FLOORDROBE   10. B**E OFF!

11. P**sed off Pets   12. Dating Profiles

13. What have you left on?

14. COMMUTER 15. A REAL Bikini Body
CRUSH      16. Washing up

17. Makeup bag Breakdown  18. Meditation

19. Moths vs Cardigans

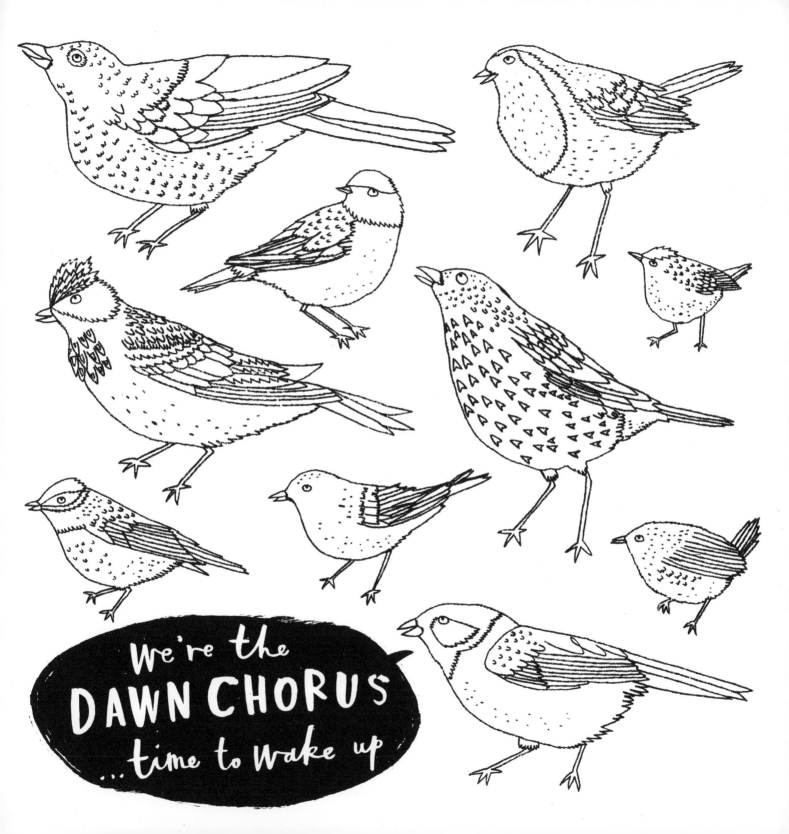

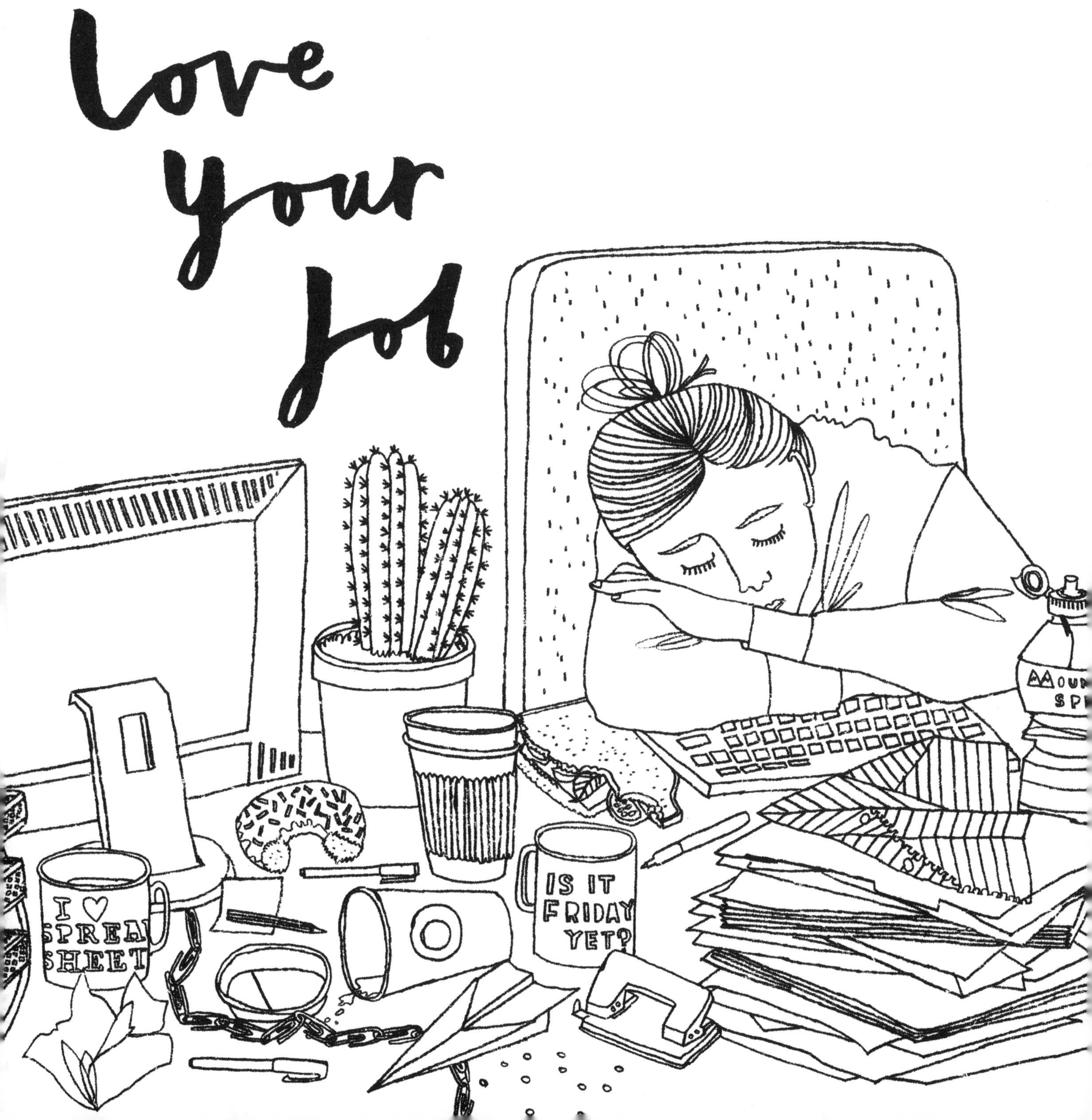
Love your Job
IS IT FRIDAY YET?

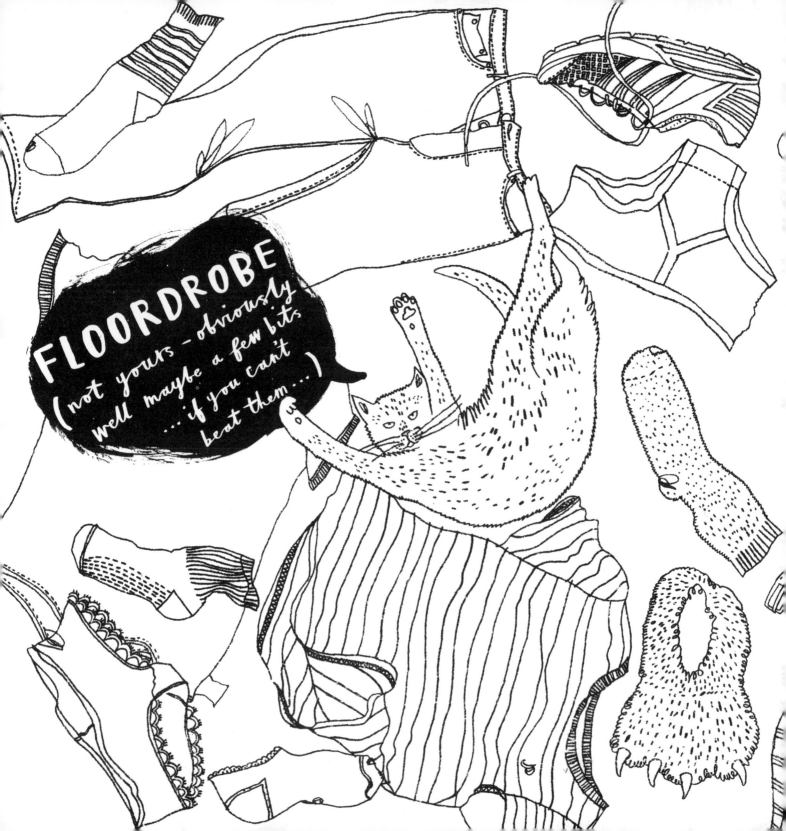

Dating

Profiles

When did you take that?

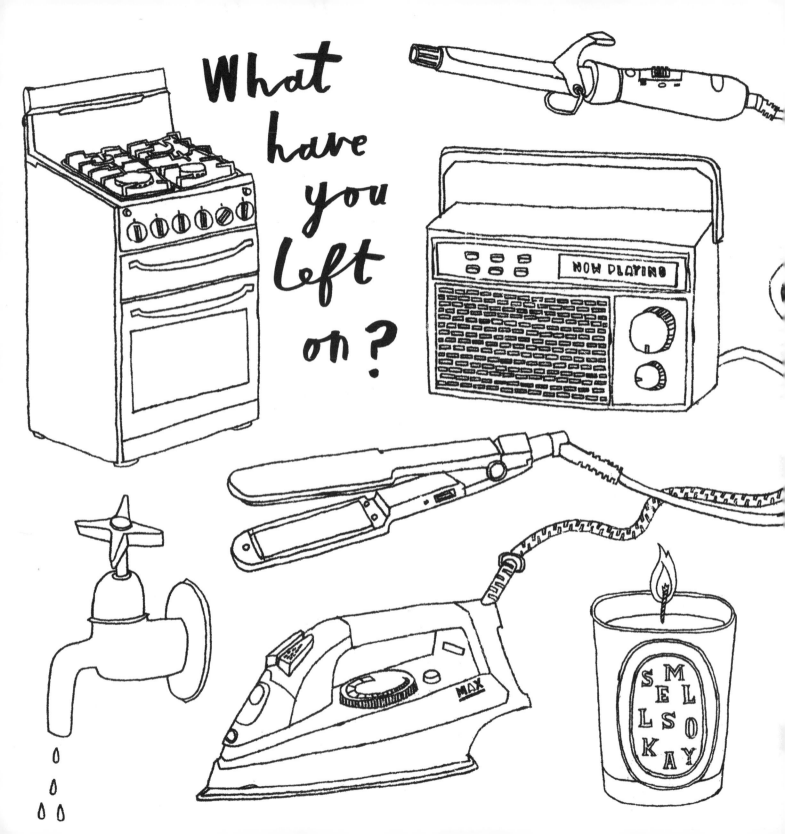

...and did you even lock the door?

COMMUTER CRUSH

Obstructing
the doors
can be
dangerous

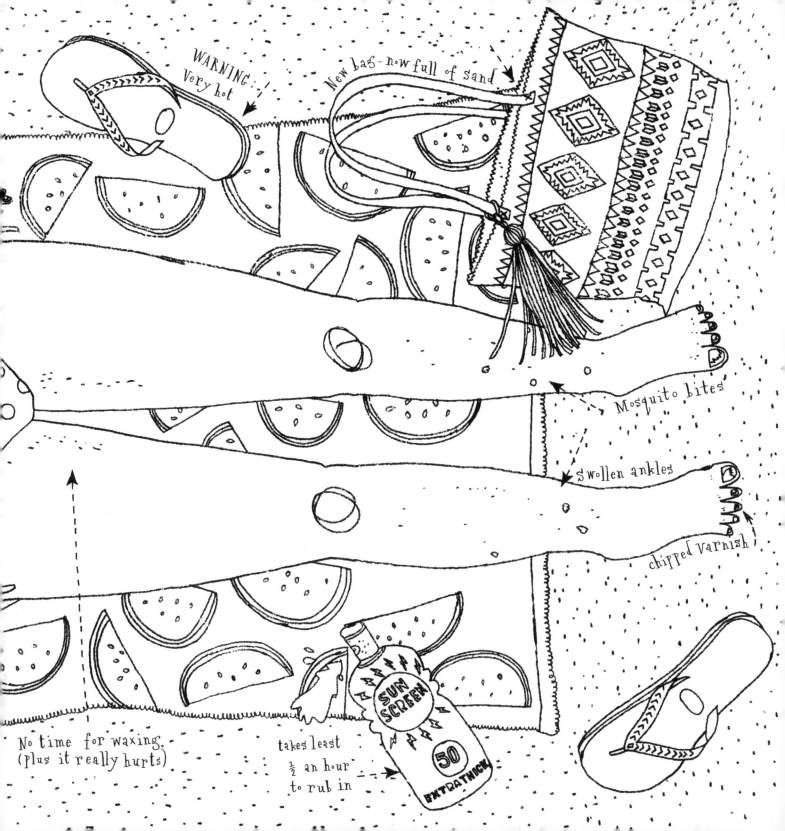

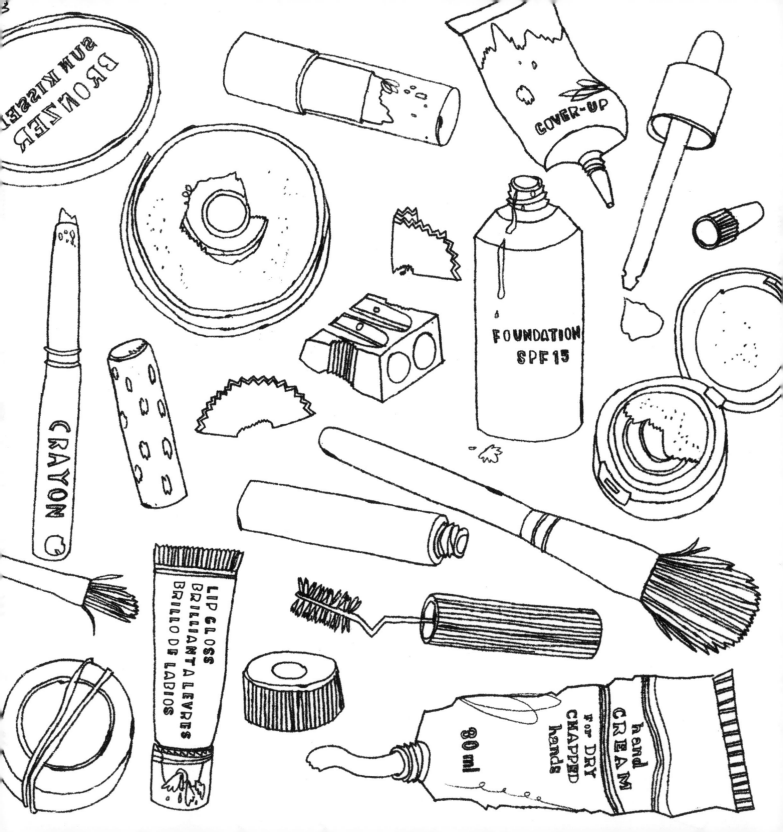

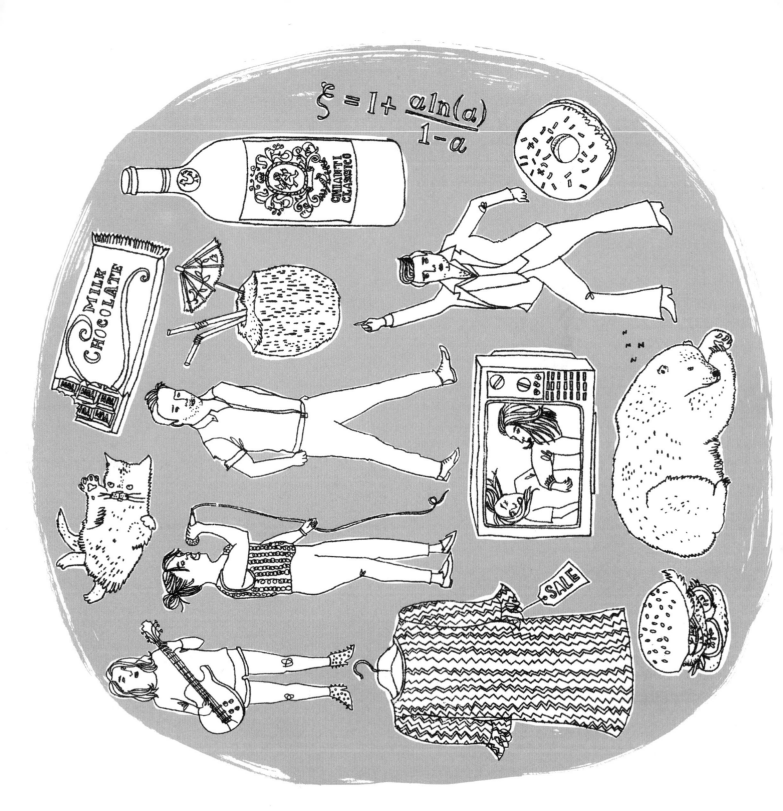

Meditation

Clear your mind...

Moths vs Cardigans

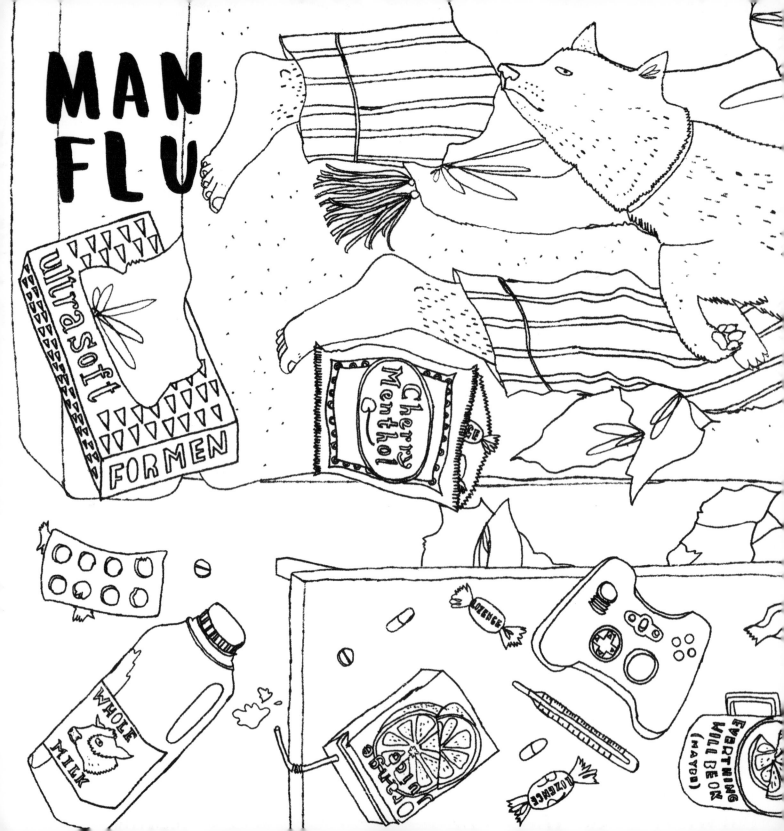

# Pin Bored

Stretch Run
○ Exercise

Quiet home

my style

too much cute
○ animaux

Princess
○ Hair

25 mindful LEMON DETOX RECIPES

Healthy mind & Body

Reality

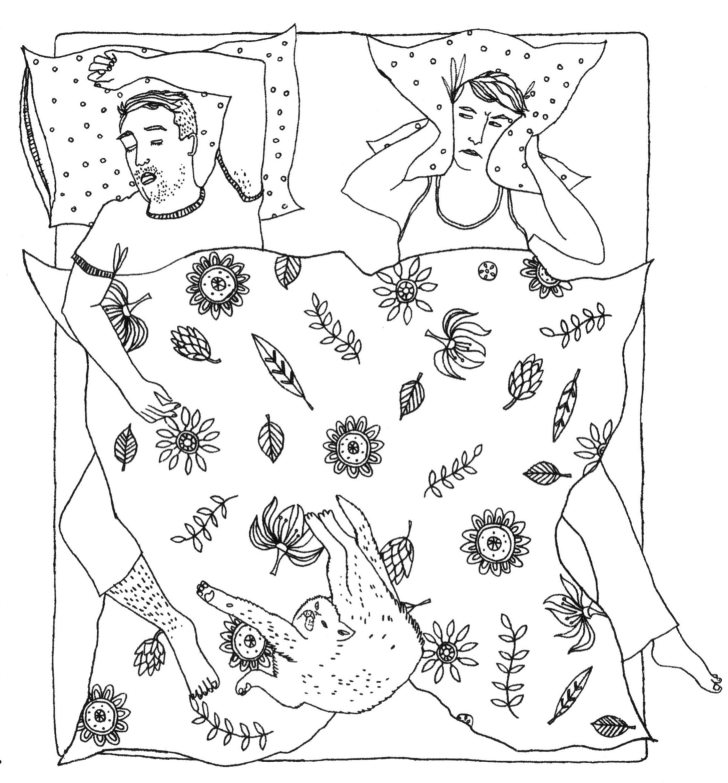

PASSIVE-AGGRESSIVE SLEEPING PATTERNS

Dried-out wet wipes

Lemon Wet Wipes

3 PLY TISSUES

Lip balm covered in fluff

escaped tampon

(not used but out of wrapper)

book ruined by water

THE Milk THIEF

MARK MUZAK

DAIRYMILK

THE MILK THIEF

used tissue

Receipt x 20 ish
507160

fluff-covered mint

CHOCOLATE

Loves his hobby more than you

I ♥ MY

Mama's
Boy
(& Mama
didn't
like you
much)

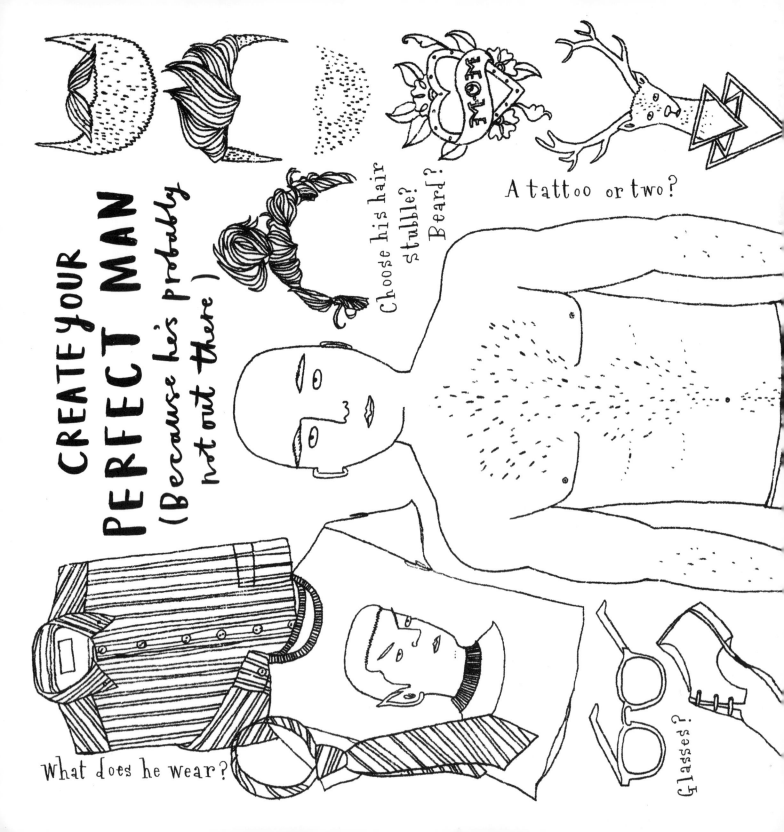

# CREATE YOUR PERFECT MAN
## (Because he's probably not out there)

Choose his hair

Stubble? Beard?

A tattoo or two?

What does he wear?

Glasses?

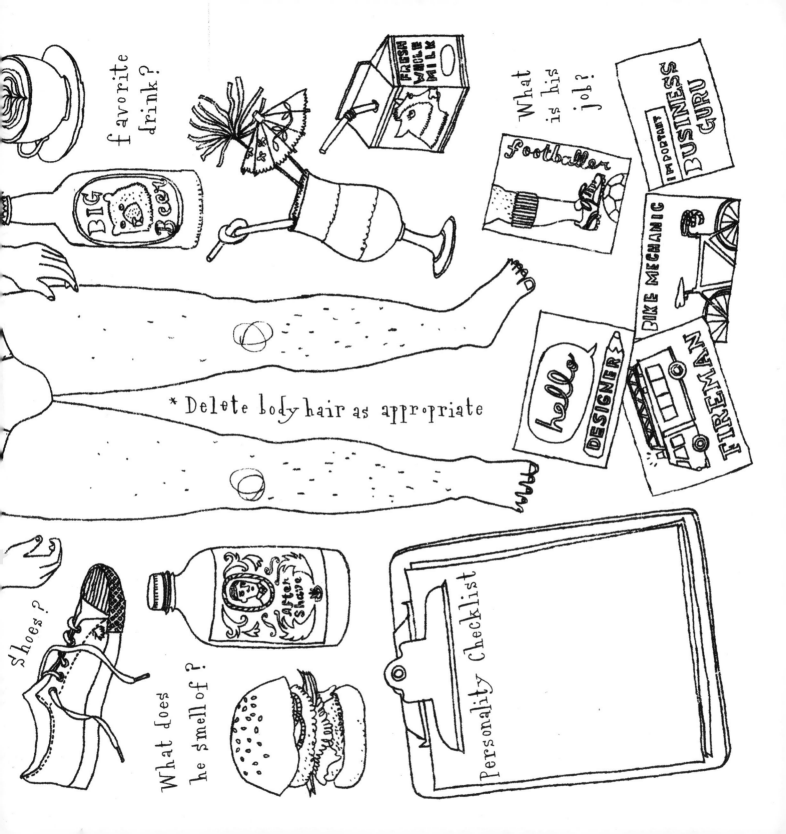

# Acknowledgments

MEEOW

## thanks

Pat - for putting up with any passive aggressive-ness from me during the making of this book and Margo - who is either aggressive or asleep!

Also thanks to the Ilex team: Rachel (hope you find a ripe 'ripe & ready' avocado one day), Zara, Frank, Roly & Julie